foreward

The Arizona we call home is comprised of many diverse and beautiful environments. While the soil, plants, and animals vary from our deserts to our pine forests and from our farmlands to our urban centers, there is one natural gift that we are all fortunate to receive in abundance—sunlight. Enjoying hundreds of sunny days every year, it can be easy to take this largely invisible gift for granted. Fortunately for us, Sasha and Rodney's Jeremy Jackrabbit is here to remind us of the many valuable and innovative ways that we can harness the power of the sun to help our communities survive and thrive.

Whether we embrace solar technology to grow our food, dry our laundry, or power our homes, schools, and offices—like we do at Arizona State University—we as Arizonans are uniquely privileged to benefit from such a clean and plentiful source of energy. Moreover, we continue to find new and more efficient ways to use our brilliant sun to make life better and more sustainable. As demonstrated here by the charming artwork of Arizona students, we can all find a way, big or small, to incorporate this natural resource into our daily lives and in turn, make our state stronger and brighter for generations to come.

Michael M. Crow, *President*
Arizona State University

about jeremy jackrabbit

The character of Jeremy Jackrabbit was inspired by a poster that hung on Rodney's little brother's bedroom wall that read, "Jeremy Jackrabbit Juggles Jumbo Jelly Beans." And, ever since Jeremy was a child, he has always loved the color green. As the champion of the nation's first mandatory rainwater harvesting ordinance, Rodney and his wife, Sasha, decided it would be an enjoyable and worthwhile community project to write a children's book educating students about the importance and ease of rainwater harvesting. In the spring of 2010, Jeremy Jackrabbit came to life with the distribution of 15,000 copies of *Jeremy Jackrabbit Harvests the Rain* throughout Southern Arizona.

In 2012, Sasha and Rodney shared their concept for their second children's book, *Jeremy Jackrabbit Recycles the Can* with friends from the Phoenix Public Library, Superintendent Tim Ham from the Madison Elementary School District, and the Caliber Group—all who offered to collaborate on making the couple's new vision a reality. During the fall of 2012, over 100,000 young people throughout Maricopa County were invited by the Phoenix Public Library, City of Tempe Public Library, and local school districts to submit illustrations of various sections of the text that Sasha and Rodney had written. The result was the distribution of over 56,000 copies of *Jeremy Jackrabbit Recycles the Can* to over 50 elementary school districts across Arizona.

With the success of their second book, commitments from additional corporate sponsors, an enhanced partnership with Arizona State University, and the announcement of *Jeremy Jackrabbit Captures the Sun*, the Jeremy Jackrabbit book series was born. Since each page of the book is illustrated by a different student artist, Sasha and Rodney called on their friend and Southern Arizona artist, Catalina Rankin, to illustrate a formal version of Jeremy that could be used to promote their children's book and provide additional continuity. The Caliber Group, Catalina Rankin, and the dozens of children who illustrated these pages have donated their time and talents to make this project a success. After months of work, what resulted was not simply a children's book on solar energy, but rather a piece of community artwork for everyone to enjoy!

Printed in Tucson, Arizona, USA

Book design by The Caliber Group
Jeremy Jackrabbit illustrations by Catalina Rankin
Printed by Arizona Lithographers
Published by Dandak Publishing, LLC. Meridian, Mississippi

CleanWatts   Energy CERTIFIED
Printed with *100% New Wind Energy*

this book
belongs to:

_____

this book is dedicated to...

UFCW Local 99 President Jim McLaughlin, Plumbers & Pipefitters Local 469 President Phil McNally, Phoenix City Councilman Michael Nowakowski, Madison Elementary School District Superintendent Dr. Tim Ham, Arizona State University's Director of the Global Institute of Sustainability Patricia Reiter, City of Tempe Deputy Public Works Director John Osgood, and the Phoenix Public Library's Rita Hamilton, Rita Marko, and Wendy Resnik for their consistent and unwavering support of the Jeremy Jackrabbit book series; and Leslie and Andrew Feldman, Amy and Richard Blum, Carrie and Tom Ryerson, Flo and Paul Eckstein, Patrice and Rob Pickering, Ray Jensen, State Representative Jeff Dial, and Barbara and Barry Zemel for their support and friendship.

It is also dedicated to Catalina Rankin, Kerry Stratford, Linda Welter Cohen, Liz Tanori, and The Caliber Group for making our vision a reality!

Special thanks to President Michael Crow, Rick Shangraw, and Ginny Foltz from Arizona State University for their partnership; Kelly Saunders from the Arizona State University Global Institute of Sustainability for designing teacher lesson plans based on Jeremy's story; Pilar Kelley for her beautiful translations; and Maricopa County Superintendent of Public Education Don Covey, Peter Gorraiz, Billy Whitaker, Tracy Bame, Clarissa Cerda, Deb Griffith, Maja Wessels, and Gene D'Adamo for their investment, feedback, and support.

With much love to Rodney's brother, Jeremy, for inspiring our lead character and to our countless friends for their candid, critical feedback!

Sasha and Rodney Glassman

Jeremy Jackrabbit

Captures the Sun

la liebre Jeremy
Aprovecha el Sol

by:
Sasha and Rodney Glassman

illustrations by:
Student Artists of Arizona

Jeremy Jackrabbit lived in the DESERT
and he loved the color GREEN,

Jeremy Jackrabbit vivía en el desierto y le encantaba el color verde;

1

h e would HARVEST THE RAIN, and then use it AGAIN,
saving water for his GARDENING.

Una y otra vez, con mucha energía y algarabía la lluvia recogía,
ahorrando agua para su huerto.

With his FRIENDS he'd play games,
such as toy trucks and trains,
flying kites when the DESERT winds blew,

Con sus trenes y tractores con sus amigos jugaba,
y volaban sus cometas cuando los vientos del desierto soplaban,

But when hopping one day, he did not want to play,
because his GARDEN was making him BLUE.

Pero saltando un día, se dio cuenta que su huerto no crecía, y no quiso jugar más.

"**M**y PLANTS won't grow TALL, they are scraggly and small, and the clouds make my GREEN PLANTS look gray.

"Mis plantas no van a crecer, están delgadas como un alfiler, y las nubes hacen que mi huerto verde se vea gris.

With no VEGGIES or FRUIT, my garden's kaput,
though I WATER it every day."

Aunque riegue mis plantas cada día, sin frutas ni verduras, mi huerto es una locura."

"**h**ow can my plants **GROW** high as an elephant's eye?"
Jeremy asked **RUTHY THE KANGAROO RAT**.

"¿Cómo puedo hacer que mis plantas crezcan tan altas como la luna,
una por una?" Jeremy pregunto a Ruth el Canguro.

"**Y**ou should CAPTURE THE SUN, it shines for EVERYONE,"
Ruthy squeaked as she gave him a pat.

"*Deberías aprovechar el sol, el brilla para TODOS,*"
Ruthy chirriaba mientras lo apapachaba.

"CAPTURING RAYS is the key," buzzed down **BARRY THE BEE.**
"It's what FEEDS ALL THE PLANTS and the trees."

"Aprovechar los rayos del sol es la clave," dijo Barry la Abeja mientras susurraba.
"Los rayos del sol son los que alimentan los árboles y plantas."

"**W**ithout sun don't you know,
nothing GREENISH would GROW,
and then there'd be no FLOWERS FOR BEES!"

"Nada verde crecerá, las flores y abejas desaparecerán, sin la energía del sol!"

With a very strong will, and a DESERT FOX NAMED PHIL, Jeremy worked hard to get the job done.

Con mucha entereza y sin nada de pereza, el Zorro Phil del Desierto y Jeremy, trabajaron sin descansar para poder trasplantar.

his tomatoes and beets,
corn and strawberries so SWEET,
were replanted to get better SUN.

Sus tomates y fresas, remolacha y maíz, estaban ahora muy feliz aprovechando los rayos del sol.

12

In a short span of time, his PLANTS started to climb, toward the SUNLIGHT up his garden wall;

En poco tiempo, sus plantas crecieron, ya que la energía del sol recibieron;

Jeremy asked, "Is there MORE that the SUN has in store?" And his DESERT FRIENDS heeded his call.

"¿Qué más ofrece el sol y su energía para ayudar a la ecología?"
pregunto Jeremy, y sus amigos del desierto pronto respondieron.

In her RED FIRE TRUCK, pulled up ROSIE THE RECYCLING DUCK,
she was quacking and flapping with speed,

Rosi el Pato, en su rojo camión, hablaba de su estación con mucha pasión,

"**O**n our roof panels lay, **CAPTURING SUNLIGHT** all day, for the **POWER** our station might **NEED**."

"En la estación de bomberos, paneles solares tenemos, la energía aprovechamos y el medio ambiente ayudamos."

16

Just then GILA MONSTER MIKE,
peddling his BRIGHT YELLOW BIKE,
pulled round quickly while keeping wheels spinning.

De repente llego Gila Monster Mike, en su bicicleta amarilla.

"Using **SUN TO DRY CLOTHES** is free everyone knows, just hang them outside," he hissed happily grinning.

"Secar la ropa al sol es una maravilla para la economía, es gratis y fácil," dijo mientras sonriente siseaba.

nd with a loud howl, flew **BOB THE BURROWING OWL**,
it was **DARK** as he came in much later,

En la oscuridad, con un gran ulular volando llego el sabio Búho Bob,

hen I go to MATH class, one way I always pass,
is because of my SOLAR CALCULATOR."

"En Matemáticas, con mi calculadora solar,
siempre saco puras A's y me dan ganas de volar."

"I've got just the ticket," chirped **CARRIE THE CRICKET**, **"when COOKING you can use the SUN'S HEAT."**

"Dando un brinquillo," llego Carrie el Grillo, "cuando cocinas puedes usar el calor del sol."

"Just take MIRRORS and LIGHT, and aim them just right, and turn BATTER TO CAKE you can eat."

"Con los rayos del sol y un par de espejos, habrá gran festejo.
Si los pones en la dirección correcta, masa convertirás en pastel y será un deleite comer."

"When it's time for a SWIM," snorted JAVELINA JIM, "sometimes WATER can be a bit chilly."

"La alberca fría, me enfermaría," gruño Jim el Jabalí.

23

"**B**ut with **SOLAR** near your **POOL**,
warming water can be **COOL**,
any other way would just be plain silly."

"La energía solar, el agua calentara y la alberca a todos divertirá."

JEREMY JACKRABBIT was DELIGHTED,
for all his friends had recited,
he could GROW, COOK, GO SWIMMING, and PLAY.

Jeremy Jackrabbit a sus amigos escucho gustoso,
y descubrió que aprovechar los rayos del sol lo hacía dichoso.

With the SUN in the SKY, life was sweeter than pie, he could HARNESS EACH and EVERY RAY.

Con los rayos del sol, cosechar, cocinar, nadar, y jugar seria grandioso.

26

ow everyone knows how CAPTURING the SUN'S POWER goes
and how to "LIVE GREEN" all the year through.

Ahora todos saben que cada día tenemos que cuidar la ecología.
Aprovechar los rayos del sol ayudaría y todo verde se vería.

So make it a habit, be like JEREMY JACKRABBIT,
and start CAPTURING the SUNLIGHT too!

Como Jeremy Jackrabbit, que se te vuelva costumbre,
aprovechar los rayos del sol para que el ¡mundo deslumbre!

blue barrel recyclables

Please recycle the items shown below.
All material must be clean, dry, and empty.

glass
Bottles and jars with no lids/caps
(green, amber, and clear)

aluminum / metal
Beverage cans, aluminum foil, tin food cans, and foil
food containers (frozen dinner trays and pie plates)

plastics
Containers with recycle emblem 1-7 with lids/caps
placed separately (2-liter bottles, milk, detergent,
water bottles, and clear food containers); no
styrofoam or plastic bags

cardboard
Food boxes such as cereal, cake mix, and cracker
containers (remove liners), beer and soda carriers,
shoe boxes, and milk and juice cartons;
no food/grease residue

corrugated boxes
Folded-flat boxes with removed styrofoam,
packing peanuts, and plastic

magazines and newspapers
Remove metal/plastic binding. Include inserts.

junk mail
Window envelopes and newspapers, including inserts

phone books

shredded paper
Place in clear plastic bag and tie up

29

bote azul reciclables

Por favor recicle los articulos mostrados abajo. Todo el material debe estar limpio, seco, y vacío.

Vidrio
Botellas y frascos sin tapadera (verde, ámbar, y transparente)

aluminio / metal
Envases de refrescos, papel de aluminio, latas de comida, y bandejas de aluminio para comida (bandejas de comidas congeladas y moldes de pai)

plásticos
Envases con emblema de reciclaje 1-7 con las tapaderas puestas separadamente (botellas de 2 litros, envases de leche, jugos, detergente, botellas de agua, y recipientes transparentes de comida); ningún poliestireno o bolsas de plástico

cartón
Cajas de comida como cereales, mezcla de pastel, y cajas de galletas saladas (quite las bolsas), cajas de cerveza y refrescos, cajas de zapatos, y cartones de leche y jugo; ningún residuo de comida o grasa

cajas de cartón corrugado
Doble las cajas planas y quite los empaques de poliestireno, nieve seca, y plástico

periódicos y revistas
Incluyendo encartes.
Quite la encuadernación de metal o plástico

propaganda de buzón
Sobres con ventana

guías telefónicas

papel triturado
Coloque en una bolsa de plástico transparente y amárrela

page illustrators

contributing illustrators

Alexis Alonso

Yuridia Ballesteros

Iaxon Brown

Pedro Ceron

Xavier Ramon Fausto

Corin Friese

Hayden Gertchen

Lauren Keena

Carmelita Trujillo

Sarah Lynd

Ariana Martinex

Chloe Mcintosh

Blake Melcher

Maliah Navarro

Sebastian Ortega-Nunez

Sandy Parra

Brianna Pecak

Trinity Powell

Victoria Solano

Dineh Thornton

Marquairrah Salazar

Mia Vargas

Emma Wood

sponsors

CITY OF TEMPE ARIZONA®

THE ARIZONA REPUBLIC
azcentral.com

ASU GLOBAL INSTITUTE of SUSTAINABILITY
Walton Sustainability Solutions Initiatives

First Solar.

FREEPORT-McMoRan COPPER & GOLD

LifeLock®
Relentlessly Protecting Your Identity®

UFCW 99

United Phoenix Fire Fighters Association

UA — PLUMBERS · UNION · PIPEFITTERS · SPRINKLERFITTERS · STEAMFITTERS · SERVICE TECHS

supporting sponsors

Foundation for Teaching & Learning

CHANDLER EDUCATION FOUNDATION

MCESA
Maricopa County Education Service Agency

community partners

ASU Foundation for A NEW AMERICAN UNIVERSITY
ARIZONA STATE UNIVERSITY

CALIBER
MARKETING · PR · INTERACTIVE

MADISON EDUCATION FOUNDATION
PHOENIX, ARIZONA

little **BIG**minds
Spanish Immersion Preschool

Yours to Explore
PhoenixPublicLibrary
www.phxlib.org